Psycho

ROBERT BLOCH

Level 3

Retold by Chris Rice
Series Editors: Andy Hopkins and Jocelyn Potter

GW00776310

Pearson Education Limited
Edinburgh Gate, Harlow,
Essex CM20 2JE, England
and Associated Companies throughout the world.

ISBN: 978-1-4058-7689-6

First published in Great Britain by Robert Hale 1960
This adaptation first published by Penguin Books Ltd 1998
Published by Addison Wesley Longman Ltd and Penguin Books Ltd 1998
New edition first published 1999
This edition first published 2008

5 7 9 10 8 6 4

Acknowledgements
The publisher would like to thank the following for their kind
permission to reproduce their photographs:
The Kobal Collection: PARAMOUNT 2, 4, 7, 10, 13, 18, 26, 29, 31, 39

Cover image: Corbis: Bettmann

Typeset by Graphicraft Ltd, Hong Kong
Set in 11/14pt Bembo
Printed in China
SWTC/04

Published by Pearson Education Ltd

For a complete list of the titles available in the Pearson English Readers series, visit
www.pearsonenglishreaders.com.
Alternatively, write to your local Pearson Education office or to Pearson English Readers
Marketing Department, Pearson Education, Edinburgh Gate, Harlow, Essex CM20 2JE, England.

Contents

Introduction

A hotel, here, in the middle of nowhere? Impossible. She closed her eyes and opened them again. Yes, it was true. There it was. A small sign shining in the night:

BATES MOTEL

'I don't believe it,' she said to herself as she drove towards the sign. 'This is my lucky night.'

Marion Crane is a secretary from Phoenix, Arizona. She is in love with Sam Loomis, who lives far away in Fairvale, Texas. She wants to marry him. But Sam cannot marry her because he doesn't have enough money. So Marion steals $40,000 from her boss and drives towards Fairvale with the money. It's a long, dangerous journey and, not far from Fairvale, Marion gets lost. It's dark, it's raining, and she's tired and hungry. If she can find somewhere to stay for just one night, then all her troubles will be over.

But as Marion drives towards the small quiet motel by the side of the Old Highway, something terrible is waiting for her there.

Alfred Hitchcock (1899–1980) made the film *Psycho* in 1960. Other Hollywood film-makers believed that the book, by Robert Bloch, was impossible to film. But Hitchcock had different ideas. Working in black and white, he made one of Hollywood's most frightening films ever.

Robert Bloch was born in Chicago in 1917. His first book, *The Scarf*, came out in 1947. He wrote many mystery and science fiction books and stories for television. He also wrote the films *Psycho II* (1982) and *Twilight Zone: The Movie* (1983). He died in Los Angeles in 1994.

Chapter 1   Marion and Sam

In a small, dark hotel room in Phoenix, Arizona, Marion Crane was looking at herself in the mirror. She was worried. Her hair was untidy and she was late getting back to work.

'Don't go, Marion,' said a voice from behind her.

Marion looked in the mirror at the young man who was sitting on the bed. She smiled at him sadly. 'I must get back to the office, Sam,' she said. 'My boss is beginning to get worried about these long lunch-hours.'

'But it's Friday afternoon,' Sam said. 'I don't see you very often. Can't you stay?'

'When we're married,' Marion replied, walking across the room to pick up her handbag.

Sam jumped off the bed and stood behind her. He touched the side of her face softly with the back of his hand. 'Can I see you next week?' he said.

'Why?' she said, not looking at him. 'For another secret lunch, hoping that nobody will see us together in a small, cheap hotel room? It's the same every week.'

She turned to Sam, her eyes shining angrily. And then suddenly they softened. 'Oh, Sam,' she said quietly. She rested her face in his hand as she looked up into his eyes. 'Why can't we get married now? I want to be with you all the time. I want to walk along the street with you so that everyone can see us together.'

This time, Sam walked away. He stood alone by the window and looked down at the hot, dry city. 'We can get married when I've paid off all my father's debts,' he said. 'I only need to pay another $11,000.'

'And how long will that take?'

Marion sighed and turned round in his arms to rest her head against his shoulder. 'In three years, I'll be twenty-nine,' she thought unhappily.

'Two years, maybe three.'

'Oh, Sam,' Marion cried, throwing the handbag onto the bed and running to hold him. 'I can't wait three years. I don't care about the money.' She kissed his face, but she was almost crying. 'I want to be with you. I'll leave my job. I'll come and work in your shop.'

'Marion, please. You must understand. I don't want us to be poor when we get married. I want us to be happy. In three years' time, you'll be my wife – Mrs Sam Loomis. I promise.'

Marion sighed and turned round in his arms to rest her head against his shoulder. 'In three years, I'll be twenty-nine,' she thought unhappily.

Then she suddenly remembered that she was late for work. She left Sam by the window, picked up her bag and walked towards the door. 'I have to go, Sam,' she said again. 'I'm late. Mr Lowery will kill me.'

Chapter 2   Marion's Plan

'I'm sorry I'm late,' Marion called as she hurried into the office.

'Don't worry,' the other secretary said. 'Mr Lowery's having lunch with a customer.'

Marion gave the other woman a tired smile and sat at her desk. 'Did anyone phone while I was out?' she asked.

'Just your sister. She says that she's going away for the weekend . . .'

Just then Mr Lowery walked in. He was talking to a loud-voiced man in a cowboy hat. Marion immediately looked down and tried to look busy. She knew Tommy Cassidy and she didn't like him. He was an unpleasant, greedy old man who was always talking about money.

Cassidy sat down on Marion's desk and showed her a

Cassidy took a thick packet of money out of his pocket and waved it in front of Marion's face. '$40,000,' he smiled proudly.

photograph of his daughter. 'She's eighteen years old,' he said. 'And she's never been unhappy.'

Marion looked at the photograph and then at Cassidy. She didn't like the way that he was looking at her, with his clear, cold eyes and his wet, smiling lips.

'She's getting married next month,' he said, 'and I'm buying her a house.' He took a thick packet of money out of his pocket and waved it in front of Marion's face. '$40,000,' he smiled proudly. 'This will make her happy, won't it?'

Marion looked at the money and smiled politely.

'Are you happy, Marion?' Cassidy asked, still holding the money in front of her.

Marion wanted to stand up and shout at him: 'How can I be happy? I can't get married for three years while Sam works to

4

pay off his father's debts. But you're rich! You can make $11,000 in three weeks. It isn't right!'

But she didn't say any of this, of course. She sat at her desk and smiled sweetly. 'I think so, Mr Cassidy,' she said.

'I hope you are,' Cassidy said, putting the money on the desk. 'Remember, Marion. Money can't buy happiness, but it can stop unhappiness.'

He walked away into Mr Lowery's office, but Mr Lowery didn't follow him. He was looking at the money on Marion's desk and seemed worried. 'I don't want that money here over the weekend,' he said to her quietly. 'Take it to the bank after work.'

'Perhaps I can take it now?' Marion asked. 'I've got a terrible headache.'

'Good idea,' Mr Lowery agreed. 'Take the money straight to the bank, then go home and have an early night.'

Marion put the money into a white envelope, put the envelope into her handbag, and left the office.

But she didn't take the money to the bank. A plan was taking shape inside her head. '$40,000 is a lot of money,' she thought. 'With this money, Sam'll be able to pay his debts. Then we'll be able to get married.'

Pleased with this idea, Marion went straight home. She put some clothes into a suitcase, and drove out of Phoenix.

As she was waiting at some traffic-lights for people to cross the road, Marion looked at the bag next to her with the money in it. 'Of course,' she was thinking, 'I can't tell Sam that I stole the money from my boss. I'll have to think of a good story to tell him . . .'

Suddenly one of the people crossing the road stopped in front of her car. It was Mr Lowery. Without thinking, Marion smiled at him and waved. He looked at her seriously, then walked away.

'Oh no!' Marion thought. 'Now he knows I haven't gone home with a headache. If he thinks I'm running away with the money, he'll phone the police. I must hurry. If I can get to Fairvale before Monday, they'll never find me. I'll be safe with Sam.'

It was a long journey. After driving all night across the desert, Marion began to feel tired. She had to stop. She drove off the highway and parked at the side of a quiet road. 'I'll just rest for half an hour,' she told herself.

But she was more tired than she thought. She lay down in the front of the car and slept until the morning.

Chapter 3   Bates Motel

Marion woke up suddenly. A policeman with a thin mouth and large dark glasses was looking at her through the car window. Without thinking, she sat up and turned the key to start the car. The policeman knocked on the window and told her to stop. Marion opened the window and looked at him nervously.

'Is anything wrong, miss?' the policeman asked.

'No. I was feeling tired so I stopped the car.'

'Why didn't you stay at a hotel? There are lots of hotels near here.'

'I only wanted a rest,' said Marion. 'Why? Have I done anything wrong?'

'No, miss,' the policeman replied, but he wasn't happy. 'Can I see your driving papers please?'

Marion turned away from him and opened her bag. The policeman tried to watch over her shoulder, but he didn't see the white envelope full of money. She hid it carefully under her bag, then handed him her driving papers. He studied them for a minute, gave them back and, without a word, returned to his car.

Marion started her car immediately and drove away. Looking

Marion turned away from the policeman and opened her bag.
The policeman tried to watch over her shoulder.

in her driving mirror, she noticed that the police car was following her. She drove slowly so that it could go past, but it stayed behind her. 'Why's he following me?' Marion thought nervously. 'Has Mr Lowery reported me already? If he has, I'll have to sell this car as soon as I can and get another one. I don't want anyone to follow me to Fairvale.'

At last the police car stopped following her, and turned off along another road. About an hour later Marion arrived in a small town. She stopped at a garage and asked about changing her car for another one. While the man from the garage was looking at her old car, Marion walked out into the street to buy a newspaper. Then she noticed the policeman with the dark glasses. He was standing by his car across the road, watching her.

Marion didn't look at him. She bought a newspaper and looked through it quickly. 'Good,' she thought. 'There's nothing in the paper about me or the money. Nobody knows yet. That policeman doesn't know anything. He's just trying to frighten me.'

She went back to the garage and showed the man the car that she wanted.

'Don't you want to try it first?' he asked.

'No thank you,' Marion replied. 'I'm in a hurry. How much will it cost?'

'Your car, and seven hundred dollars.'

Marion went to the washroom and took seven hundred dollars from the white envelope. She came out and gave the money to the man, who looked at her strangely. Then she jumped into her new car.

'Just a minute, miss.'

Marion's heart jumped. She looked round quickly, but it was only another man from the garage. He was carrying her coat and suitcase.

'You left them in your old car,' he explained, putting them in the back of her new one.

As Marion drove away, the policeman crossed the road and stood next to the man from the garage.

'Did she seem strange to you?' the policeman asked.

'Very strange,' the man agreed.

♦

Marion drove across the desert all day, then up into the hills. As it got dark, it began to rain. Tired and hungry, she looked hard through the window for somewhere to stay the night. She couldn't see anything in the heavy rain. No lights along the road, no other cars. 'I think I'm on the wrong road,' she thought. 'If I turn round and find the highway again, I'll soon find a place to stay.'

Suddenly, as she was looking for a good place to turn the car, she saw a light by the side of the road. At first she thought she was dreaming. A hotel, here, in the middle of nowhere? Impossible. She closed her eyes and opened them again. Yes, it was true. A small sign shining in the night:

BATES MOTEL

'I don't believe it,' she said to herself as she drove towards the sign. 'This is my lucky night.'

Chapter 4   Norman

There were no other cars outside the motel, and the office was empty. Marion stood outside the office and waited. Looking up, she saw a large old house on a hill behind the motel. On the first floor of the house she could see a light in a window. There was a shadow moving behind the curtain. The shadow of a woman, Marion thought.

She went back to her car and waited for someone to come.

At last, through the darkness and the rain, she saw someone

Marion saw a large old house on a hill behind the motel.

outside the house. It was a man, and he was running down the hill towards the motel. Marion got out of her car to meet him. He was a young man, tall and thin, with a friendly, boyish face.

'I'm sorry I wasn't in the office,' he smiled.

'Do you have a room?' Marion asked.

'Twelve rooms, all of them empty,' the young man laughed. 'You're wet. Come into the office.'

Inside the office, the young man watched her carefully as she wrote her name in the visitors' book. Not her real name, but: 'MARIE SAMUELS'. Then he thought for a second before choosing a key from the small cupboard behind the desk.

'Room One,' he smiled. 'It's next to this office.'

The young man carried Marion's suitcase from the car, and she followed him into her room. He turned on the light, and opened the window.

'It's small, but it's comfortable,' he said. 'And look. There's a shower in the bathroom.'

'Thank you, Mr Bates,' Marion smiled.

'My name's Norman,' he said. 'If you want anything, I'll be in the office.'

'I just want to sleep. But before that, I need to eat.'

'There's a restaurant about ten miles away, outside Fairvale. But I was just thinking . . .' he said, lowering his eyes with a shy smile. 'It's a long way to Fairvale and it's still raining. Maybe you'd like to have dinner with me instead? Nothing much. Just bread, milk and cheese. But you can come up to my house with me, if you like.'

'You're very kind,' said Marion.

Norman looked up, his eyes shining with excitement. 'I'll be back when everything's ready. With an umbrella!'

Marion closed the door behind him and smiled for the first time in twenty-four hours. 'What an amusing young man,' she thought. 'Just like a little boy.'

But she was tired, and she had important things to think about. The money, for example. Marion looked round the room for somewhere to hide it. There wasn't much furniture. She decided to put the envelope inside her newspaper and leave it next to the bed.

While she was doing this, she heard a loud voice. It came from the big house on the hill. She went to the window and listened. It was the angry voice of an old woman.

'No, you can't bring strange young girls up to this house.'

'Mother, please . . .' Norman replied.

'First you bring them up to the house. Then what? Music after dinner? Holding hands and kissing?'

'Mother, she's just a stranger. She's hungry and it's raining.'

'She's not having food with my son in this house. Do you understand, boy? Are you going to tell her, or shall I come down and tell her?'

'Shut up!' Norman cried. 'Shut up!'

Then everything was silent.

Chapter 5   Mad Things

Marion heard the front door of the big house as it closed. Moments later she left her room and met Norman, who was standing nervously outside her door.

'I made trouble for you. I'm sorry,' Marion said.

'No. It's my mother, that's all. She isn't well today. I'm sorry. I can't take you to the house. I've taken the food into my office. Would you like to come in there?'

Marion followed Norman into a small room behind his office. It was a strange room, full of old clocks and stuffed birds.

Norman watched her quietly as she began to eat. Then said: 'You eat like a bird.'

'I made trouble for you. I'm sorry,' Marion said.

'Do you know a lot about birds?'

'I don't know much about them. I just like stuffing them.'

'That's a strange thing to do,' said Marion.

'I enjoy it.'

'Is your time so empty?'

'No. I'm very busy. I do everything in the office, I clean the rooms. I look after my mother.'

'Have you got any friends?'

Norman looked surprised at this question. 'A boy's best friend is his mother.'

Marion looked at her bread and cheese. She couldn't think of anything to say. The room was quiet. Just the sound of the clocks.

'It's stopped raining,' Norman said.

Marion smiled politely and continued eating.

'Where are you going?' Norman tried to start the conversation again.

'Somewhere nice,' said Marion.

'What are you running away from?'

13

This time, Marion was surprised. 'Why do you ask that?'

'Oh, people are always trying to run away from something,' Norman replied. 'But people can never really run away, can they? Sometimes, when my mother talks to me like that, I want to run away. But I know I can't. She's ill.'

'She didn't seem ill to me,' said Marion.

'I mean ill in the head,' said Norman. 'My father died when I was five. She was alone with me. Then a few years ago my mother met this man. She loved him. I think she loved him more than she loved me . . .' Norman's eyes darkened as he looked past Marion at the wall. 'When he died,' Norman said slowly, 'and the way that he died . . . That's why my mother became ill . . .'

Marion felt sorry for Norman then. He was like a lost child, spending all his life in a small motel with his mad mother. 'Why don't you leave here?' she asked him.

'If you love someone, you don't leave them.'

'Then why not put her somewhere like . . .'

'Like a hospital, you mean?' Norman looked at Marion angrily. 'A hospital for mad people?'

'I'm sorry. I didn't want to be rude.'

'My mother isn't mad,' Norman said, his eyes still burning. Then suddenly, without warning, he became calm again. He smiled. 'I know,' he said, in a soft voice. 'I just hate thinking about it. My mother really isn't dangerous. She doesn't hurt anyone. She just does mad things sometimes. We all do mad things sometimes, don't we?'

His eyes met Marion's and he seemed to look straight into her heart. 'Don't you do mad things too, sometimes?'

'Yes, sometimes,' Marion smiled. She thought about the $40,000 in the newspaper in her room. She did a mad thing yesterday afternoon, when she put Tommy Cassidy's money in her handbag and ran away with it. 'I must take it back,' she thought. 'Tomorrow morning.'

14

She stood up. 'Thank you for the meal,' she said to Norman. 'I'm tired, and I have a long journey tomorrow. All the way back to Phoenix. You see, I made a bad mistake. I want to go back and put everything right before it's too late.'

Norman gave her a warm smile. 'I've enjoyed talking to you,' he said. 'I'll bring you breakfast in the morning.'

'You'll have to be early,' Marion said.

'I will, don't worry,' Norman replied. 'Sleep well.'

Chapter 6   As Clean as Snow

Marion went into her room and sat on the bed. 'Yes, it was a stupid idea to steal that money,' she thought. It was like a bad dream. Now, after talking to that strange, sweet young man, she was awake again. 'I'll take the money to the bank first thing on Monday morning,' she thought. 'Nobody will know what I've done. Everything will be all right.'

She stood up. She suddenly felt very strong and happy. She felt wonderful. 'After I have a shower, I'll feel perfect,' she thought. 'I'll be as clean as snow.'

She took off her blouse, her skirt and shoes, and threw them onto the bed. She didn't realise that someone was watching her. There was a hole in the wall between Marion's room and the one behind Norman's office. Norman was looking through the hole, watching Marion as she undressed.

Before going into the shower, Marion suddenly thought of something. She sat down at a small desk and wrote some numbers on a piece of paper. 'I spent seven hundred dollars of that money today,' she thought. 'I must try to pay that back. But that isn't important now. I'm too tired to think about money. I want a shower.'

She walked into the bathroom and threw the piece of paper

into the toilet. Then she took off her other clothes and got into the bath. Pulling the plastic curtain behind her, she turned on the shower.

It was lovely. Beautiful and warm. She closed her eyes. The warm water washed down over her body. The bad dream was over. She was becoming a good, clean girl again . . .

Marion didn't hear the bathroom door as it quietly opened. She didn't see the old woman who was slowly crossing the floor. She was facing the wall when the woman's hand pulled the plastic curtain open. She turned quickly and could see, through the water in her eyes, a face. A terrible white face with long grey hair and mad, shining eyes. And above the woman's head, in her hand, there was a large, silver knife.

Marion screamed. The woman laughed and brought the knife straight down into her neck. Marion went on screaming as the knife cut into her arms, her throat, her stomach. She tried to fight, but the old woman was too strong. The knife cut deeply into her body, again and again and again. Marion became weaker, her screams became softer. Finally, with a small, strange noise at the back of her throat, Marion dropped to the floor of the bath and lay perfectly still. Water was falling into her face, into her beautiful, frightened eyes. It washed down over her body, red with blood.

Marion Crane was dead.

Chapter 7 The Swamp

Norman felt sick when he saw the blood on his mother's clothes.

'Mother, oh God! Mother!' he cried. 'Blood! Blood!'

He ran down the stairs from his mother's bedroom, out of the house and down the hill to the motel. He couldn't believe it. His mother a killer? It wasn't true . . .

But when he finally ran into the girl's room, he saw that it *was* true. The girl was lying in the bath with her eyes still open, dead. And his mother was the killer. He stood outside the bathroom, feeling sick and afraid. He tried to think, but he didn't know what to do.

He thought about calling the police, but then stopped. He mustn't call them. Not now. Because his mother wasn't really a killer. She was sick. You were not a real killer if you were sick in the head.

No, he must stop people from knowing. He had time. The girl was alone. Nobody knew she was there. The best thing to do was to throw away the body. But how?

Then Norman had an idea. He turned off the bedroom light and the shower in the bathroom. Then he took the plastic curtain from the shower and opened it out on the bedroom floor. Next, he took Marion's body out of the bath and pulled her slowly onto the plastic curtain.

After washing the blood from the floor and walls in the bathroom, he picked the body up inside the plastic curtain and carried it out to her car. He went back to the bedroom and put everything that belonged to the girl inside the suitcase. He put that into the car with the body. He looked round the room one last time. He saw the newspaper next to the bed, picked it up and, not knowing about the money inside it, he threw that into the car too.

Then he got into the car and drove away towards a swamp not far from the motel. When he arrived, he got out of the car and pushed it into the swamp. He watched nervously as it slowly went down. It took a long time, but finally it disappeared.

Norman smiled. 'Mother's safe now,' he thought. 'Nobody will ever learn what happened to the girl.'

Norman stood outside the bathroom, feeling sick and afraid.

Chapter 8   Lila

One week later, Sam Loomis was sitting in the office at the back of his shop, writing a letter to Marion. 'Since I saw you last Friday afternoon,' he wrote, 'I've thought a lot about the things that you said. You're right. The money doesn't matter. I want to marry you now...'

While he was writing, Bob Summerfield, the young man who worked in the shop, called to him: 'Sam, a young woman wants to see you.'

Sam walked into the shop and saw a pretty young woman with fair hair and a small suitcase.

'I'm Lila, Marion's sister,' she said without smiling. 'Is she here?'

'Of course not,' Sam replied. 'Is something wrong?'

'I haven't seen her since last Friday,' Lila said, her voice beginning to shake. 'She left home without saying anything. She hasn't even phoned me. Look, if she's here, I want to talk to her. She's in bad trouble.' She began to cry.

Sam told Bob to leave the shop, then turned to Lila. 'Tell me,' he said softly. 'What are you talking about? What kind of trouble is she in?'

'Yes,' said a flat, unfriendly voice from the door behind them. 'Let's all talk about Marion.'

Sam and Lila both turned to see who was talking. A short man with a hat low over his eyes walked slowly into the shop. He was carrying a raincoat over his arm.

'My name's Arbogast,' he said, showing them a card. 'I'm a detective, but I'm not with the police.' He looked hard at Lila and said: 'Now Miss Crane, where's Marion?'

'Why do you want to know?' said Sam.

'$40,000,' Arbogast replied.

'I don't understand.'

19

'Your girlfriend stole $40,000.'

Sam looked at Lila. 'Is this true?'

Lila explained everything. She spoke in a cold voice. She still believed that Sam was hiding Marion somewhere. But when she finished, her voice softened. 'Listen, Sam,' she said. 'Her boss doesn't want to call the police. He just wants his money back. So if she's here . . .'

'She isn't,' Sam said quickly.

'Miss Crane, can I ask you a question?' said Arbogast.

'Why did you come here to Fairvale? Did you know that your sister was here?'

'I hoped she was. I wasn't sure.'

Arbogast looked at her and said nothing.

'It's true!' she cried angrily. 'Why don't you believe me?'

'I'm just doing my job, Miss Crane.'

'Really?' said Sam. 'Then have you phoned any hospitals near Phoenix? Maybe she's had an accident.'

'That's not possible,' Arbogast replied. 'Her boss saw her in her car last Friday. She was driving out of Phoenix with the money.'

Then Arbogast looked at Lila. He gave her a warm, friendly smile to show that he finally believed her. 'I think she's here, Miss Crane,' he said. 'Maybe not here with her boyfriend, but she's somewhere near Fairvale. I can feel it. Don't worry,' he said, touching his hat and walking towards the door. 'I'll find her.'

Chapter 9   A Few Questions

The next day Arbogast visited all the hotels near Fairvale. He showed everyone a picture of Marion. 'Have you seen this girl?' he asked them. The answer was always 'No.'

At last, as he was driving along the Old Highway outside Fairvale, he saw a small motel by the side of the road.

'Maybe I'll be lucky with this one,' he thought. 'I've tried all the others.'

Arbogast left the road and drove up to the motel. Norman Bates was sitting outside his office in the evening sun, reading a magazine. He stood up and smiled as Arbogast got out of his car.

'I almost missed you,' Arbogast said.

'I forgot to turn on the sign,' Norman replied. 'Do you want a room?'

'No thanks. I only want to ask a few questions.'

'What sort of questions?' asked Norman, turning to go into his office.

'I'm trying to find a girl,' said Arbogast, following him. 'My name's Arbogast. I'm a detective.'

'Oh really?' Norman tried to smile calmly. 'A girl?'

'Her name's Marion Crane,' Arbogast explained. 'She's from Phoenix. She disappeared last Friday and her family are very worried.' He showed Norman the photograph. 'Have you seen her?'

Norman shook his head without looking.

'Maybe she stopped here about a week ago?'

'No. I haven't had any visitors for more than two weeks. Business has been bad since they moved the highway.'

'Can I see your book?'

Norman gave him the book from under the desk without speaking. He watched as Arbogast took out an envelope and studied the names in the book.

'Ah.' Arbogast's finger stopped at the name of Marie Samuels from Los Angeles. 'You see? She *was* here last Saturday night. Look. The writing is the same as on this envelope.'

'So?' Norman said in a weak voice.

'The writing on this envelope belongs to Miss Crane.'

Norman opened his mouth to speak, but his mouth was dry and he couldn't think of the right words. Finally he said: 'It's difficult sometimes.'

Arbogast looked at Norman. 'What's difficult?'

'Remembering things.'

'I know, I know,' Arbogast said softly, trying not to frighten him.

'You know, I wasn't lying, mister. I just forgot about last week.'

'I understand.'

Arbogast's friendliness seemed to make Norman calmer. He smiled, and asked to see the photograph again. This time he studied it carefully.

'Oh yes,' he said. 'I remember now. It was raining. This girl arrived late at night. She was tired and went straight to bed. She left early the next morning.'

'Did she meet anybody here?'

'No, she was alone.'

'Did she phone anybody?'

'No.'

'How do you know?'

Norman shut his eyes. It was happening again. His face was burning and he couldn't think of an answer. Finally he said: 'She was tired. She said she wanted to go straight to bed because she had a long journey the next morning. And now, Mr Arbogast, I'm very busy. I have to go.'

'One more question, please,' Arbogast said as Norman began to walk away. 'Is she still here?'

'No, she isn't. I told you before. If you don't believe me, I'll show you all the rooms.'

'No, that's all right,' Arbogast smiled.

He followed Norman outside. It was dark now. He looked up at the house on the hill and noticed a light in a window.

'Is anyone at home?' he asked, as Norman was walking away.

Norman turned round and smiled. 'No.'

'But there's someone sitting by that window.' Arbogast pointed at the house.

'Oh, that's my mother. She's ill.'

Arbogast looked hard at Norman for a moment, then said: 'Did that girl offer you a lot of money?'

'What do you mean?'

'To hide her here, maybe?'

'Look mister, if you think I kidnapped her or something . . .'

'I'm not saying that. But perhaps she offered you money and asked you not to tell anyone? Maybe she told you some stupid story . . .'

'Mr Arbogast, I'm not stupid,' Norman said.

'No, of course you're not. But sometimes it's just too easy to believe a pretty girl.'

'Even if I'm stupid, my mother isn't,' Norman was getting excited again. 'My mother didn't believe anything she said.'

'So your mother met her?' Arbogast looked surprised. 'Can I meet your mother too? I'd like to talk to her.'

'No you can't. I told you. She's sick.'

Arbogast wanted to talk to the mother, but there was something strong and icy about Norman now. He decided not to push him. 'I'll come back later,' he thought. 'After I've phoned the girl's sister and told her what I know.'

Chapter 10   Shadow Behind the Curtain

After phoning Lila with the news of his conversation with Norman Bates, Arbogast drove back to the motel. There was a light in the office, and the sign was now on, but he couldn't find Norman anywhere. Looking up at the old house, he could still see the old woman by the window. He could see her shadow behind the curtain.

'I'll have to go and speak to her without her son's help,' he thought.

After climbing the hill, Arbogast found that the front door was open. He walked inside, took his hat off and waited for a few seconds. Everything was quiet. He looked at the mirror, the flowers on the wallpaper, the old pictures on the wall.

Feeling sure that the son was busy somewhere, he decided to go upstairs and talk to the mother alone. He walked up the stairs very slowly. He didn't want to make a noise. And, if he was honest, he felt a little afraid. With its old furniture and silent rooms, this house was very strange.

At the top of the stairs, Arbogast heard the sound of the bedroom door. He turned round and saw the old woman. She was running straight towards him, with her long dress, white face and cold, mad eyes. He was too surprised to move. He saw the large silver knife above her head, and he tried to lift his hands, but he was too late.

The knife cut his face open from the top of his head, through his left eye, to the corner of his mouth. He fell back, down the stairs, and lay very still. He couldn't move his arms or legs, but he could lift his head. With his one good eye he looked up the stairs – the old woman was flying down towards him, the silver knife in her hand, screaming like an animal. The last thing that he ever saw was the terrible white face above him, as she brought the knife down straight into his heart.

Chapter 11   A Visit to the Sheriff

Sam and Lila sat in the room behind the shop, waiting for Arbogast to return.

'It's over an hour,' said Lila. 'Why isn't he back yet?'

'Maybe he found something important.'

Lila pushed back her chair and stood up. 'He's more than an hour late. He hasn't even called. I'm going to the Old Highway. I know he's found something. Are you coming with me?'

Sam stood up with a sigh. 'I'll go. You stay here,' he said. 'Somebody must be here if Arbogast comes back.'

The motel was dark and empty when Sam arrived. He called Arbogast's name several times, but nobody answered. He looked up at the big house behind the motel, and saw somebody at the window. 'I guess that's the mother,' he thought. 'The old woman that Arbogast wanted to speak to.' He climbed the hill and tried the door. Again, no answer.

Sam drove back to Fairvale. 'There's nobody at the motel,' he told Lila. 'No Arbogast. No Bates. Just a sick old woman who couldn't answer the door.'

'I'm worried,' Lila said. 'Something's wrong.'

'I agree,' said Sam. 'We have to tell the police. Let's visit Jud Chambers. He's the sheriff of this town. He'll be able to help us.'

The sheriff and his wife had to get out of bed to answer the door. It was late, but they asked Sam and Lila to come in. They listened while Sam told them about Marion and Arbogast.

'Arbogast phoned us to say that he wanted to go back to the motel. He wanted to speak to Mrs Bates,' said Sam. 'But that was three hours ago.'

'I didn't know that Norman had a wife,' said Mrs Chambers, surprised.

'No,' Sam explained. 'It's an old woman. His mother.'

The sheriff thought for a minute, then asked Lila: 'When did your sister disappear?'

'She left Phoenix a week ago.'

'How did you know that she came here?'

'She came to see me,' Sam explained.

'And she didn't say anything to you?' the sheriff was still looking at Lila.

25

'No. She just ran away.'

'From what?'

Nobody spoke for a moment. Then Lila said quietly: 'She stole some money.'

'A lot?'

'$40,000.'

'Why didn't you tell the police before?'

'We wanted Marion to give back the money without telling the police.'

'Did this detective talk about the money when he phoned you three hours ago?'

'The money doesn't matter, does it?' Lila cried unhappily. 'I just want to find my sister!'

The sheriff sighed, and tried to look friendly. 'What can I do?'

'I'm sure there's something wrong,' said Lila. 'At the motel, I mean.'

Mrs Chambers looked at Lila and she felt sorry for her. 'Why don't you telephone Norman at the motel?' she said to her husband.

'Norman? It's Sheriff Chambers speaking. Listen, I have some people here. They're worried. Did you have any visitors tonight?'

'It's late.'

'Oh, please call,' said Lila.

The sheriff sighed again and picked up the telephone. 'Hello?' he said a few seconds later. 'Norman? It's Sheriff Chambers speaking. Listen, I have some people here. They're worried. Did you have any visitors tonight? . . . No, not a customer . . . a detective . . .'

Jud Chambers listened quietly for a minute, then put down the phone. 'Yes,' he said, turning to Sam and Lila. 'The detective was there tonight. Norman told him about the girl. The detective said thank you and left.'

'Without seeing Mr Bates's mother?' Lila asked.

The sheriff looked Lila straight in the eye. 'Norman's mother died ten years ago.' He said. 'She killed her lover, then she killed herself. It was in all the newspapers. Norman found them dead together, in bed.'

'But that isn't true. I saw her!' Sam cried.

'Yes,' Lila agreed. 'Arbogast saw her too.'

'Mm,' Jud Chambers replied, looking at his wife. 'Very strange. If Norman's mother is still alive, who was the woman who killed herself ten years ago?'

♦

Norman Bates put down the phone after speaking to Sheriff Chambers. 'The police will be here soon,' he thought. 'I must hide Mother before they come.'

He ran out of the office, up the hill to the old house, and climbed the stairs to his mother's room.

'Mother, I have something to say,' he said.

The old woman laughed. 'You're a stupid boy, telling me what to do.'

'Mother, it's important.'

'No. I will not hide in the fruit cellar. I'm staying here. This is my room and no one will ever take me away.'

'They'll come for you, Mother,' Norman tried to explain. 'That man came after the girl. Now someone will come after him. Mother please, just for a few days, so that they won't find you.'

'A few days in that ugly old cellar? No! You hid me there once before. I'll never go there again. Now go away!'

But Norman wasn't listening. He picked his mother off the bed and carried her out of the bedroom, down the stairs, and into the fruit cellar.

Chapter 12   Room One

The next day, Sunday morning, Sam and Lila met Jud Chambers and his wife as they were coming out of church.

'Do you want to go to the motel with us?' Lila asked.

'I went before breakfast,' said the sheriff.

'What did Mr Bates say about my sister?'

'The same as he told your detective. I promise you, Miss Crane, Norman Bates is alone at the motel. I looked everywhere.'

'You didn't even see his mother?'

'No, I didn't. I'm sorry. If you want the police to help you, you'll have to make a report in the usual way. You can see me this afternoon, if you like. I'll be happy to help you.'

'Well,' said Sam, after saying goodbye to the sheriff and his wife. 'Maybe I was dreaming and Arbogast was lying. Perhaps I saw a shadow on the curtain, that's all.'

'You weren't dreaming and Arbogast wasn't lying,' Lila told him. 'There's something wrong, and I'm going to the Bates Motel immediately. Come on.'

Sam and Lila drove quickly to the motel on the Old Highway. While Sam looked for Norman Bates in the office, Lila stayed outside. She was interested in the house on the hill. There was something dark and strange about it, even in the morning sunshine. Suddenly she saw a tall, thin man at the top of the hill. He stood still at first, then he began to walk quickly down the hill towards her. Lila called to Sam, who ran out of the office.

Norman Bates wasn't surprised to see the young man and woman outside his office. He walked down the hill towards them with his hands in his pockets.

'Do you want a room?' he asked them pleasantly.

'Yes, please,' said Sam.

'Then follow me,' Norman smiled, walking past them into his office.

'Is Room Ten okay?' he asked, taking the key from the small cupboard on the wall behind the desk.

'I'd like to write my name in the book first,' said Sam.

'Okay.' Norman took the book from under the desk and gave it to Sam.

While Sam was writing his name, Norman watched Lila. She was looking at the list of names in the book. 'I know who you

Norman took the book from under the desk and gave it to Sam.

are,' Norman thought. 'You're looking for the man who came yesterday. Well, you can look. You won't find anything. I've hidden everything. And you'll never find my mother in the cellar. But I mustn't make any mistakes. I must be careful . . .'

He took the book and pen from Sam. 'Thank you,' he smiled. 'Now I'll get your bags.'

'We haven't got any.'

'Okay. I'll show you to your room.'

'Don't worry,' said Sam, taking the key. 'We'll find it.'

When Sam and Lila were alone in their room, Lila sat on the bed and began to cry. 'I know something terrible has happened to Marion,' she said. 'Seeing that old house on the hill, the way that man kept looking at us. I can feel it.'

'I agree,' said Sam. 'But we need to find something to show the police. Let's go and search Room One. That's the room that Arbogast said she stayed in, isn't it?'

Sam and Lila opened the door and looked outside. They couldn't see anyone. Hoping that nobody was watching them, they hurried nervously back, past the other rooms, to Room One.

They searched everywhere for some information about Marion. Something to show that Bates knew where the money was, perhaps. They found nothing in the bedroom, so they went into the bathroom.

'That's interesting,' Sam said. 'No shower curtain.'

Suddenly, Lila noticed something. 'Look,' she said, picking a small piece of paper out of the toilet. It was wet, but she could still read something on it. 'It's a number. Forty thousand.' She looked at Sam. 'This shows us that Marion *was* here.'

'We know that already,' said Sam.

'You don't understand. It shows us that Bates knew about the money.'

'Okay. I'll talk to him,' Sam said, and walked towards the door.

30

But Lila stopped him. 'No,' she said. 'Let's talk to that old woman in the house. She told Arbogast something, and I want her to tell me the same thing. You find Bates and talk to him. I'm going to talk to his mother.'

Sam wasn't happy about Lila's plan, but he agreed.

Hoping that nobody was watching them, they hurried nervously back, past the other rooms, to Room One.

Opening the door, he looked out. 'It's clear,' he said to Lila. 'No one's watching. You can go.'

Sam quietly shut the door as Lila ran towards the hill. He found Bates in his office.

'Are you looking for me?' Bates asked.

'Yes,' said Sam, standing in front of Bates so that he couldn't see Lila. 'I'm bored – my wife's asleep and I wanted to talk to someone.'

'Good,' Norman smiled. 'Come in and shut the door.'

Chapter 13   The House on the Hill

Lila climbed the hill to the old house, and pushed the front door. It opened slowly. She walked inside and shut the door behind her. It was sunny outside, but inside the house it was strangely cold and dark. There was an unpleasant smell of dry wood and old furniture.

'I mustn't be afraid,' Lila thought. 'I must find the old woman. She can tell me about Marion. Maybe I'll even find my sister here.'

So, thinking about her sister, Lila bravely began to move towards the stairs.

♦

'You don't talk very much, do you?' Sam said to Bates in the motel office.

Bates, with his hands in his pockets and his back against the wall, laughed nervously.

'I thought that people who lived alone enjoyed talking. You're alone, aren't you?'

'Yes.'

'I hate being alone,' said Sam. 'When I'm alone, I go mad.'

Norman stopped smiling. 'Why do you say that?'

'I think that people who live alone go mad,' Sam answered, feeling quietly pleased. The smooth young man with the boyish smile was beginning to look uncomfortable. 'Don't you agree?'

Norman's face went red.

◆

Lila arrived at the top of the stairs and knocked on the bedroom door.

'Mrs Bates?' she called softly.

There was no reply, so she pushed the door open and walked inside. She couldn't believe her eyes. Everything was so old, from the heavy curtains by the window to the golden lamps on the darkly coloured walls. She walked across the room nervously towards the large cupboard with a mirror on the door. Opening the door, she saw a line of long, flowery dresses. The kind of dresses that women wore fifty years ago.

Lila closed the cupboard and looked round the room. Her eyes rested on a small table near the bed. She looked at the small glass cats, the silver soap-dishes, the old photographs of children . . . or were they different photographs of the same child?

Everything was very old, but there was something even more unusual than this. Everything was so tidy. This was very strange.

'If this is the mother's bedroom,' Lila thought, 'why doesn't she touch anything? The only thing that she seems to use is the bed. I can see from the bedclothes that she was here a short time ago. So she's here somewhere. But where?'

◆

'I don't think you're happy here,' Sam told Bates. 'Why don't you sell this place and leave?'

'This place is my world,' Bates said. 'I grew up in that house. I was a happy child. My mother and I were very happy!'

♦

Lila looked inside another room. It was a small room with an untidy bed and lots of books and children's things on the floor.

'Norman's room,' she thought, picking up some of the books. They were about the mysteries of life and strange illnesses. Looking at the unusual books and the children's play-things on the floor, Lila thought that she was beginning to understand something about Norman. 'He's a little boy who loves his mother,' she thought. 'An intelligent boy who has never grown up.'

♦

'You look nervous,' Sam told Bates. 'Have I frightened you?'

'What are you talking about?'

'I've said something about your mother, and you look afraid. How are you going to do it?'

'Do what?'

'Buy a new motel. You won't have to hide your mother if you go to another town.'

Norman's eyes became cold and narrow. He hated this man and wanted him to go.

'Where will you get the money?' Sam continued. 'Or do you already have the money? $40,000 perhaps?'

Bates walked into the room behind the office, and Sam followed him.

'Your mother knows about the money, doesn't she?' Sam said. 'She knows what you did to get it. And I think she'll tell us.'

Bates turned round, his eyes burning, his heart racing. 'I know why you're here,' he shouted. 'Where's that girl who came here with you?'

Sam said nothing. He turned away and began to walk out of the door. This was a mistake. Bates ran up behind him and hit him hard on the head with a metal box. Sam fell to the floor, and Bates ran out of the office as quickly as he could.

'I must find that girl before she finds Mother,' he thought, as he ran up the hill towards the old house.

Chapter 14   The Cellar

When Lila came back down to the bottom of the stairs, she looked through the window by the front door and saw Bates. He was running up the hill towards the house. She had no time to ask herself about Sam. She had to hide.

As Lila ran towards the kitchen, she heard Bates at the front door. Suddenly she noticed some stairs. They seemed to go down towards some kind of cellar. Without thinking, she ran onto the top stair and waited.

Bates stood still for a second. He couldn't see Lila, but he knew she was in the house. Probably upstairs, looking for his mother.

Lila stood up when she heard Bates upstairs in his mother's room. Now she could escape and find Sam. But she couldn't stop looking at the cellar door below her. Maybe the mother was down there? Perhaps Marion and Arbogast were prisoners down there? She had to go down to learn the secrets that were hiding behind that door.

It was dark inside the cellar, and there was a strange smell of dead animals and oil. She stood still for a few seconds. Then she thought she could see a light on the opposite side of the room. It was coming from underneath a door. She walked slowly towards it in the dark, past tables full of glass bottles, knives and tins. At last, she came to the door and opened it slowly.

It was a small room with one light in the ceiling. In the middle of the room there was a wooden chair facing the opposite wall,

35

and on the chair there was a woman. Lila looked at the back of her head. She seemed to be asleep.

'Mrs Bates?' Lila said quietly. She didn't want to frighten her. 'Mrs Bates?' she said again, moving slowly towards her.

The woman didn't answer. Lila touched her shoulder. Lila turned the woman's chair round and looked down at her face. The first thing that she saw was the woman's teeth. They were large and yellow. And then Lila realised that the old woman had no eyes. She was looking down at the dry, brown face of a dead woman.

Lila screamed. She turned to run away but stopped. There was a tall, shadowy shape by the door. The shadow had long grey hair and wore a flowery dress. As it moved into the light, Lila could see the face: a white face with a terrible smile and mad, shining eyes.

Then she saw the knife. She wanted to scream again but her mouth was dry and she felt too weak. She moved back as the mad old woman ran towards her, laughing wildly, the silver knife in her hand, ready. . .

Then another person ran into the room and jumped on the mad woman from behind. Sam! He put one arm round the woman's neck and with his other hand he held her wrist, fighting for the knife. The woman fought hard, screaming wildly. But Sam was too strong for her.

Lila watched them as they fought. And then something unbelievable happened. As Sam pulled the old woman to the floor, the long grey hair slowly fell to one side of her head. Lila suddenly realised that the face wasn't the face of a woman. It was Norman Bates! And he was screaming like a woman!

Lila pressed herself against the wall. She felt sick. And Norman Bates's mother, a dead woman with no eyes, watched with a wide smile on her brown face. She seemed to be laughing at her son as he lay screaming on the cold, stone floor.

Chapter 15 'Look at that Fly on My Hand'

Some time later, Sam and Lila sat with Jud Chambers in his office. The room was full of people, all of whom were listening to a man who was talking to them about Norman.

'I got all the story,' Doctor Steiner said. 'But not from Norman. I heard it from his mother.'

'I don't understand,' said the sheriff.

'I know it's difficult, but I'll try to explain,' Doctor Steiner replied. 'You see, there *is* no Norman Bates. Not now. There never was *one* Norman Bates. He was half Norman, half his mother. Now he's all his mother. He'll probably never be Norman again.'

'Did he kill my sister?' Lila wanted to know.

The doctor looked at her sadly. 'Yes. I'm sorry. He killed Arbogast too. If we look in that swamp near the motel, I think we'll find both of them. We'll probably find other dead people too. Pretty young women, just like your sister.'

The doctor looked at all the serious faces in the room, and began to explain: 'We have to remember that, ten years ago, Norman killed his mother and her lover. He lived alone with his mother and she was the boss. Then she met another man, and Norman was jealous. He thought that his mother loved this other man more than she loved him, so he killed both of them. A short time later he went out one night, dug his dead mother out of the ground, brought her back to the house and hid her in the cellar. He looked after her like one of his stuffed birds.

'But keeping his mother's dead body was not enough. Norman soon began to think like his mother, to talk like his mother, to *be* his mother. She became half of him. Sometimes he was Norman, sometimes he was his mother, and sometimes he was both at the same time. He had to talk to himself.

'He was never all Norman, but he was sometimes all mother.

37

When he liked a girl, the mother side of his head became angry. His mother was jealous of him because he was jealous of her when she had a lover.'

Doctor Steiner turned to Lila. 'When he met your sister, he thought she was beautiful. He wanted her. That was a problem for the mother side of him. There was a fight inside his head between the two of them, but his mother won because she was stronger. So he suddenly became his mother, and his mother killed Marion. When Marion was dead, Norman woke up after a kind of deep sleep, and really believed that his mother was the killer. He put your sister's body in the swamp because he loved his mother, and wanted to save her from the police.

'When danger came too near, Norman put on his mother's clothes. He walked round the house, sat in her chair by the window and talked in her voice. He tried to be his mother, and now he is. The fight inside Norman's head is finished. The stronger person has won. He is now his mother.'

'And what about the money?' said Jud Chambers. 'Who got that?'

'The swamp,' Doctor Steiner replied.

♦

Somewhere in the same building, two policemen were standing guard outside a door. Behind the door there was a small white room with no furniture or windows. Norman Bates was alone in that room. He was sitting very still, with a strange smile on his face.

Perhaps this person was Norman Bates: he had Norman's face, Norman's body, Norman's clothes. But it was really his mother who was alive. Norman was really dead now.

'It's sad when a mother has to tell the police about her son,' the voice inside Norman's head was saying. 'They'll put him in prison now. He belongs in prison. A bad boy, who looked through holes in the wall and killed people. He thinks that *I* did all those bad things. He tried to tell that to the police. But they know it wasn't me. I've never done anything bad. I was like one of his stuffed birds. I could only watch. I couldn't stop him. I couldn't move.

'Look at me. I can't even move a finger. And I'm not going to try. I'm going to sit here very still. I'm not going to move. I'll never move again.

'They're probably watching me now. They'll see the sort of person that I really am. I'm a kind person. The sort of person who can never hurt anyone. Look at that fly on my hand for example. I'm not going to kill it. I can't.

'I hope they're watching. Then they'll see, and they'll know. And they'll say: "Look at her. She's a good woman. She can't even kill a fly." '

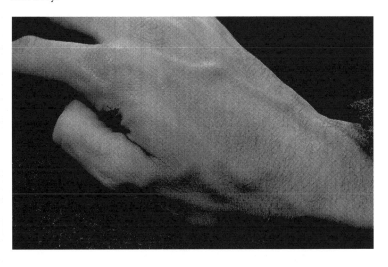

'Look at that fly on my hand. I'm not going to kill it. I can't.'

ACTIVITIES

Chapters 1–3

Before you read

1 Look at the Word List at the back of this book. Answer these questions with words from the list.
   a Where do tired drivers often stop for the night?
   b In which place do you find a lot of water?
   c Which three words can describe a person?
   d Which thing do you find inside a room?
   e Which word is a part of the body?
2 Read the Introduction to this book and answer these questions.
   a Where is Marion Crane going? Why?
   b How does Marion feel when she sees the Bates Motel?
   c Why is the film of *Psycho* famous?
3 Look at the pictures in Chapters 1–3. Who do you think the men are in each picture? Why?

While you read

4 Write the correct name. Who:
   a has to pay his father's debts?   ....
   b is Marion's boss?   ....
   c is a greedy old man who is always talking
      about money?   ....
5 Put these sentences in the correct order. Write 1–5.
   a After driving all day, Marion finds a room at
      the Bates Motel, in the middle of nowhere.   .....
   b After Marion decides to steal the money,
      Lowery sees her in her car.   .....
   c Cassidy shows Marion $40,000 for the house
      that he is buying for his daughter.   .....
   d Mr Lowery tells Marion that she should take
      the $40,000 straight to the bank.   .....
   e After the policeman follows Marion, she
      decides to change her car for another one.   .....

After you read

6 Discuss these questions.

   a How does Sam feel about marrying Marion?

   b Why does Cassidy show Marion his money and talk about his daughter, do you think?

   c Is Marion a happy person, do you think? Why (not)?

   d Why doesn't she want to tell Sam she stole the money?

   e What mistakes does Marion make? What will happen as a result of these mistakes, do you think?

Chapters 4–6

Before you read

  7 Read the titles of Chapters 4–6 and look at the pictures. What will Marion find at the Bates Motel, do you think?

  8 Do you think she will continue her journey to Fairvale? Why (not)?

While you read

  9 Are these sentences right (✓) or wrong (✗)?

   a While Marion waits outside the motel office, she sees a shadow behind the curtain of the house on the hill.   .....

   b Marion writes her real name in the visitor's book.   .....

   c Norman shows Marion the shower in the bathroom.   .....

   d After Norman invites Marion to eat with him, Marion puts the $40,000 in an envelope in her suitcase.   .....

   e Marion hears an old woman's voice talking angrily to Norman.   .....

10 Which of these are very important to Norman? Put a (✓) next to the correct answers.

   a stuffed birds .....

   b his friends .....

   c his mother .....

   d clocks .....

   e Marion .....

   f the $40,000 .....

41

11 Answer these questions. Write 'Yes' or 'No'.

    a Does Marion decide to drive back to
       Phoenix with the money? ....

    b Does Marion think that a shower will
       make her as clean as snow? ....

    c Does Norman watch Marion through a
       hole in the wall? ....

    d Does the old woman talk to Marion in
       the bathroom? ....

    e Is Marion murdered in the shower? ....

After you read

12 What do you think about Norman? Why does he:

    a give Marion Room One?

    b show Marion the shower?

    c want to have dinner with Marion in the house on the hill?

    d say, 'A boy's best friend is his mother.'

    e stay in the house with his mad mother?

13 Think about Marion's final hours. What does Marion:

    a think of Norman?

    b plan to do with the money?

    c write on a piece of paper?

    d do with the piece of paper?

    e do when she sees the knife in the old woman's hand?

Chapters 7–9

Before you read

14 Why did the old woman kill Marion, do you think?

15 Look at the picture on page 18. What will Norman do when he finds Marion's body?

While you read

16 Finish sentences a–e. Write 1–5.

   a Norman takes Marion's body out of the bath and ...   .

   b Norman picks up the newspaper with the money inside
it and ...   .

   c After throwing Marion's body into the swamp, Norman ...   .

   d A week later, Marion's sister, Lila, and Detective
Arbogast ...   .

   e Arbogast searches hotels near Fairvale for Marion
and ...   .

   1) pulls her slowly onto the plastic curtain.

   2) stops worrying about his mother's safety.

   3) meets Norman Bates at the Bates Motel.

   4) throws it into Marion's car with the body and suitcase.

   5) arrive at Sam's shop.

17 What does Arbogast learn at the motel? Circle the correct word in
italics.

   a He sees Marion's *signature / handwriting* in the motel's visitor's
book.

   b Marion arrived late and there was *nobody / someone* with her.

   c Marion *met / knew* Norman's mother.

After you read

18 Why are these important to the story?

   a the swamp

   b the Bates Motel visitor's book

   c Norman's sick mother sitting by the window

19 Work with another student. Have this telephone conversation
between Detective Arbogast and Marion's sister, Lila, after he
leaves the Bates Motel.

   Student A: You are Arbogast and you have just left Norman
Bates. Tell Marion's sister about your visit to the
Bates Motel.

   Student B: You are Lila Crane. Listen to Arbogast's news about the
Bates Motel. Find out what Arbogast learned. Ask for
his opinions about Norman and where Marion is.

Chapters 10–12

Before you read

20 Read the titles of Chapters 10–12 and look at the pictures on pages 26 and 29. What do you think will happen?

21 Why does the Bates Motel have no guests, do you think?

While you read

22 Write the missing word.

    a The old woman .... Arbogast with a knife straight into his heart.

    b Sam doesn't find the .... or Bates at the motel but he sees the sick old woman at the window.

    c After the .... telephones Norman, he tells Lila about Norman's mother's death ten years ago.

    d After Norman speaks to Jud Chambers, he hides his mother in the ....

    e Sam and Lila take a .... at the motel because they want to search Room One.

    f Sam notices that there is no .... curtain.

    g Lila finds Marion's piece of paper in the .... with 40,000 written on it.

    h Sam talks to Norman in the .... so Lila can talk to the old woman in the house on the hill.

After you read

23 Who is speaking to who? Why do they say this?

    a 'But that isn't true. I saw her!'

    b 'This is my room and no one will ever take me away.'

    c 'I went before breakfast.'

    d 'I'd like to write my name in the book first.'

    e 'You don't understand. It shows us that Bates knew about the money.'

24 Do you think that the woman in the window is Norman's mother? Or is she dead? Who is the mad woman? Who was the dead woman ten years ago? Give your opinions.

Chapters 13–15

Before you read

25 Arbogast made a mistake when he went alone into the house on the hill. Will Lila's visit end in death for her too, do you think? Why (not)?

26 Read the titles of Chapters 13 and 14. Who do you think says, 'Look at that fly on my hand'?

While you read

27 Circle the best answer.

a Norman doesn't like Sam's opinion about people who live …
in motels   alone   with their mothers

b In the old woman's bedroom everything is very old and …
dirty   broken   tidy

c In Norman's bedroom, Lila discovers that Norman
lives like a …
young boy   grown up   sick old man

d When Sam makes Norman angry, Norman hits him with …
a metal box   a knife   his hand

e When Lila finds the dead old woman in the cellar, she …
dies   screams   calls Sam

f Norman runs down to the cellar …
in a flowery dress   with his mother   with a gun

28 Which of these things does Dr Steiner tell Lila, Sam and the sheriff about Norman's illness? Write ✓ or ✗.

Does he tell them that Norman:

a killed Marion and Arbogast?   .....

b probably killed other young women?   .....

c killed his mother and her lover ten years ago?   .....

d kept his mother's dead body in the cellar with his
stuffed animals?   .....

e became his mother in his mind?   .....

f was jealous when he was Norman and when he was
his mother?   .....

45

g knows that *he*, not his mother, killed Marion?   .....

h put on his mother's clothes and talked in her voice?   .....

i took the money?   .....

After you read

29 Why does Sam talk to Norman about the $40,000? What has happened to the money, does he think?

30 Why does the mother's voice in Norman's head say, 'I was like one of his stuffed birds'?

31 Where is Norman at the end of the story? Why does he say, 'I've never done anything bad'?

32 Why are these things and people important in the story?

    a Sam's father's debts

    b the room next to the office at the Bates Motel

    c blood on Norman's mother's clothes

    d Lila, Marion's sister

    e a shadow behind a curtain

Writing

33 Marion has left Phoenix with the $40,000 and Mr Lowery wants to find her. Write his description of Marion for the detective. Use the pictures in the book to help you. How old is she? What does she look like? What kind of person is she? When and where did Lowery last see her?

34 What does Marion learn about Norman Bates's family life? What does he tell her about his mother, father, house and job? Is he happy? Does he have friends or girlfriends? Why (not)? Write about Norman from Marion's point of view.

35 Norman says, 'We all do mad things sometimes, don't we?' Is he right? Write your opinion.

36 Write Sam Loomis's letter to Marion. It is one week after he last saw her. Begin 'Since I saw you last Friday afternoon, I've thought a lot about the things that you said.'

37 Marion and Arbogast think the same thing when they see the Bates Motel. She says to herself 'This is my lucky night.' Arbogast thinks, 'Maybe I'll be lucky with this one.' What does Robert Bloch, the writer, want the reader to feel about good and bad luck? Write your opinion.

38 Write a short report for the Phoenix newspaper about Marion Crane's death. Write about the money, Sam and Lila's search for Marion, and their discovery of the murderer.

39 Do you think that Norman Bates should go to prison for the murders? Why (not)? Write your opinion.

40 Imagine you are Lila Crane. Write a letter to your cousin about Marion's death. Tell her about Norman's sick mind. Tell her why you do or do not forgive him.

41 Some murderers are very kind to animals. What does that tell us about them, do you think? How does the mother inside Norman's head want to be remembered? Write your ideas about this.

42 Do you like this book? Why (not)? Write your answer.

Answers for the Activities in this book are available from the Pearson English Readers website. A free Activity Worksheet is also available from the website. Activity worksheets are part of the Pearson English Readers Teacher Support Programme, which also includes Progress tests and Graded Reader Guidelines. For more information, please visit: www. pearsonenglishreaders.com

WORD LIST

boyish (adj) like a boy

care (v) feel that something is important

cellar (n) a room under a house

curtain (n) a piece of cloth that hangs in front of a window or a shower

debt (n) money that you must pay and have not paid yet

desert (n) an area of very dry land and few or no plants

dig (v) to move earth or make a hole in it; the past is **dug**

highway (n) a wide main road between cities in the US

jealous (adj) wanting to be the only person that somebody likes or loves

kidnap (v) to take and keep somebody as a prisoner unlawfully

mad (adj) crazy or ill in the mind

mister (n) a name, in American spoken English, for a man if you don't know his name

moment (n) a very short time

motel (n) a hotel for people travelling by car

psycho (n) a person who is seriously crazy and very dangerous

sheriff (n) a chief police officer for an area in the US

sigh (v) push air out through your mouth when you are tired, bored or sad

stuff (v) to fill the body of a dead animal to keep it looking alive

swamp (n) very soft wet ground

throat (n) the inside of the neck

LONGMAN

Dictionaries

Express yourself with confidence

Longman has led the way in ELT dictionaries since 1935.
We constantly talk to students and teachers around the
world to find out what they need from a learners' dictionary.

Why choose a Longman dictionary?

EASY TO UNDERSTAND

Longman invented the Defining Vocabulary - 2000 of the most common
words which are used to write the definitions in our dictionaries.
So Longman definitions are always clear and easy to understand.

REAL, NATURAL ENGLISH

All Longman dictionaries contain natural examples taken from real-life that
help explain the meaning of a word and show you how to use it in context.

AVOID COMMON MISTAKES

Longman dictionaries are written specially for learners, and we make sure
that you get all the help you need to avoid common mistakes. We analyse
typical learners' mistakes and include notes on how to avoid them.

DIGITAL INNOVATION

Longman dictionaries are also available online at:
www.longmandictionaries.com or **www.longmandictionariesusa.com**

These are premier dictionary websites that allow you to access the best of
Longman Learners' dictionaries, whatever you do, wherever you are. They
offer a wealth of additional resources for teachers and students in the
Teacher's Corner and the Study Centre.

Better learning
comes from fun.

Pearson English **Readers**

There are plenty of Pearson English Readers to choose from
- world classics, film and television adaptations, short stories, thrillers,
modern-day crime and adventure, biographies, American classics,
non-fiction, plays ... and more to come.

For a complete list of all Pearson English Readers titles, please contact
your local Pearson Education office or visit the website.

pearsonenglishreaders.com

Printed by Amazon Italia Logistica S.r.l.
Torrazza Piemonte (TO), Italy

18577894R00034